Sister

Thank You for...

*Thank You*
*for being an*

*...sland of comfort for me.*

I felt rescued the time that you

_____

_____

_____

_____

_____

_____

_____

*Thank You*

*for knowing m*

*ke no one else can know me.*

You've always known that I

_____

_____

_____

_____

_____

_____

_____

*magical moments we shared.*

I remember when we

_____

_____

_____

_____

_____

_____

_____

_____

*Thank You*

*for seeing me*

*as I truly am.*

You've helped me accept myself as

_____

_____

_____

_____

_____

_____

_____

_____

*Thanks for*
*sharing the mang*

*wonders of the world with me.*

The day that we discovered that

_____

_____

_____

_____

_____

_____

_____

_____

*Merci beaucoup for
the many times you helped*

*...me with my homework.*

If not for you I would have never passed

_____

_____

_____

_____

_____

_____

_____

*There will always be a place for you*

*my heart.*

Thanks for

_____

_____

_____

_____

_____

_____

_____

_____

*Thanks*
  *for just*

*being you.*

You're an original when it comes to

_____

_____

_____

_____

_____

_____

_____

_____

Lemonade 10¢

*willingness to share.*

The most extraordinary loan you ever made to me was

_____

_____

_____

_____

_____

_____

_____

*Thanks to
my sister I am*

*eady to meet the world.*

You have been a great teacher to me when it came to

_____

_____

_____

_____

_____

_____

_____

*...imes of just letting me be me.*

You taught me to love who and what I am when you

_____

_____

_____

_____

_____

_____

_____

_____

*Thanks*
*for helping me to observe*

*...he smaller things in life.*

Thanks to you I now have a better appreciation of

_____

_____

_____

_____

_____

_____

_____

*Thank You*
*for making fun*

*a necessary priority.*

I have such great memories, but this is my favorite

_____

_____

_____

_____

_____

_____

_____

_____

*Thanks*
*for keeping me*

*in your life.*

We have become closer over the years because

_____

_____

_____

_____

_____

_____

_____

*p when I was feeling down.*

You always had a magical way of making me feel better. My fondest memory is

_____

_____

_____

_____

_____

_____

_____

*...orth hanging out with.*

The most fun I had with you was

_____

_____

_____

_____

_____

_____

_____

_____

*...sister that I can rely on.*

I really counted on you when

_____

_____

_____

_____

_____

_____

_____

*Thank You*
*for making*

*ur lives memorable.*

I wish we could return to the moment in time when we

_____

_____

_____

_____

_____

_____

_____

*what's important in life.*

Thank you for helping me see the beauty in

_____

_____

_____

_____

_____

_____

_____

*o proud of me.*

I needed to hear this

_____

_____

_____

_____

_____

_____

_____

*Thanks*
*for being the big sister*

*when I really needed you.*

$I$ really needed you when

_____

_____

_____

_____

_____

_____

_____

_____

*Thank You*
*for standing*

*p to the bullies in my life.*

I wanted to run away from

_____

_____

_____

_____

_____

_____

_____

_____

*hat life is what you make it.*

We have become closer over the years because of

_____

_____

_____

_____

_____

_____

_____

_____

# Thank You
## for never saying

"*I told you so.*"

W ell almost never. There were so many times you could have
said it, like the time I

_____

_____

_____

_____

_____

_____

_____

# Thank You

## for showing

*...ne how to be an original.*

You have been a great help when it came to

_____

_____

_____

_____

_____

_____

_____

*Thank You*
*for sharing*

*...pace with me.*

Our boundary lines were erased when

_____

_____

_____

_____

_____

_____

_____

*responsibility for me.*

I felt safe while we

_____

_____

_____

_____

_____

_____

_____

_____

*a friend to my friends.*

Did you know that my friend

_____

_____

_____

_____

_____

_____

_____

_____

*Thank You*

*for all those*

*moments of quiet harmony.*

The peaceful times in our lives have been

_____

_____

_____

_____

_____

_____

_____

_____

*Thank You*

*for all of the*

*wonderful memories.*

$O$ne of my favorite is

_____

_____

_____

_____

_____

_____

_____

I can't imagine
life without you

_Thank you._

Thank you for your friendship and love. You are

_____

_____

_____

_____

_____

_____

_____

© 2004 Havoc Publishing
San Diego, California
U.S.A.

Text by Maureen Webster

ISBN 0-7416-1309-3

www.havocpub.com

Made in Korea